Summer

by Bobby Lynn Maslen
pictures by John R. Maslen

Scholastic Inc.
New York • Toronto • London • Auckland • Sydney • Mexico City • New Delhi • Hong Kong • Buenos Aires

Available Bob Books® Collections:

Pre-Reader Collection

Collection 1 — Beginning Readers and Advancing Beginners

Rhyming Words and First Stories Collection

Collection 2 — Advancing Beginners and Word Families

Sight Words Collection

Collection 3 — Complex Words and Long Vowels

Ask for Bob Books at your local bookstore, or visit www.bobbooks.com.

ISBN 0-545-02692-X

12 11 10 9 8 7 6 5 4 3 21 22 23 24

Printed in China 68
This edition first printing, September 2007

It was hot.

Molly had a big hat, but
Molly was hot.

Molly's Mom had a big hat,
but Mom was hot.

Molly and Mom went to the pond.

Ducks swam in the pond.
Fish swam in the pond.

Mom put her hands in the pond.

Molly put her toes in the pond.

"Ahhh!" said Molly.

"Ohhh!" said Mom.

Molly and Mom jumped
into the pond.

"Ahhhh!" said Mom.
"Ohhhh!" said Molly.

Molly and Mom sat in the pond. The sun was hot, but the pond was not.

The End

List of 33 words in <u>Summer</u>

<u>Short Vowels</u>

<u>a</u>	<u>e</u>	<u>i</u>	<u>o</u>	<u>u</u>	<u>sight</u>
sat	went	it	hot	but	a
hat	end	in	not	sun	to
had		big	Mom	ducks	the
and		fish	Molly	jumped	was
hands			pond	summer	put
swam					her
					ahhh
					ohhh
					said
					into

<u>Long Vowels</u>

toes

90 total words in *Summer*